2 —

Jyoti's Journey

Helen Ganly

With especial thanks
to the Peerun family in Mauritius
and the children of Oxford.

Jyoti's Journey

by

HELEN GANLY

ANDRE DEUTSCH

First published in 1986 by
André Deutsch Limited
105 Great Russell Street London WC1B 3LJ

Acknowledgement
The wallpapers shown are reproduced
by the courtesy of Arthur Sanderson & Sons Ltd.

Printed in Portugal by Printer Portuguesa

This is Jyoti. She is eight years old. She was born in a village in India.

One day she did the family washing in a nearby river with other girls and
then carried it home on her head.

She passed some farmers planting seed and driving oxen.

As she walked by the school, the younger boys were sitting outside because it was so hot.

When she drew near her house, she could see her mother inside. Outside the chickens were scratching for seed.

Jyoti went in to help her mother with the cooking. Her special job was to sort the rice in a big shallow pan removing any black grains or small stones.

Jyoti's father was far away in England, so Jyoti lived with her grandmother, mother and three sisters. They often ate rice with spicy vegetables for lunch. It was considered good manners to eat with the fingers of your right hand.

Jyoti's cousin was getting married, so mother and grandmother made new clothes for the children to wear.

The three girls loved their pretty, brightly coloured clothes.

On the day of the wedding the baby was left with a friend and mother and grandmother and the three girls set out to catch the bus to town.

The outside of their cousin's house was beautifully decorated with palm leaves.

Upstairs their cousin was being dressed by her older sisters.

They wound white daisies into her shining black hair.

She looked very beautiful as a bride in her red and gold sari, with gold jewellery all over her hands and neck.

The birds sang as she left to meet her bridegroom.

It was a beautiful wedding attended by lots of friends and relations.

When they got home, a letter had come from England. Father had saved up enough money for mother and Jyoti to join him.

Baby Asha sat on the bed and watched Jyoti packing.

Finally the day came when mother and Jyoti said goodbye. Grandmother, the baby and the little sisters were going to stay with an auntie and uncle in the village.

A beautiful white aeroplane sped through the night, taking them to far away England.

After many hours they arrived at the airport. They had to wait for a very long time before they were allowed to join father. They were tired.

Suddenly, there was father. Jyoti hadn't seen him for nearly two years. He was very happy to see mother.

Father had bought a car in which he was going to take them to their new home.

Jyoti looked out of the car window and thought how grey and cold everything looked.

At last, they came to some tall brown buildings where they got out. Father said they had a small flat on the top floor.

Jyoti had a bedroom all to herself with a beautiful new bed and bedcover. She sat and looked out of the window.

She thought of all the others in India and wondered what her new life was going to be like here, in England.